10-

The Making of Fine Glass

The Making

of

Fine Glass

By SIDNEY WAUGH

ILLUSTRATED BY
John Dreves

DODD, MEAD & COMPANY
NEW YORK · 1947

LITHOGRAPHED IN THE UNITED STATES OF AMERICA
BY RICHARD L. JONES

Contents

1. INTRODUCTION   9

2. DESIGN   10

3. MATERIAL   17

4. ON BLOWING GLASS   19

5. FURNACE AND SHOP LAYOUT   21

6. TOOLS   25

7. BASIC MANIPULATIONS   30

8. MAKING A GOBLET   40

9. MAKING A DECORATIVE BOWL   49

10. GAFFERED FORMS   68

11. CUTTING   73

12. ENGRAVING   77

13. TYPICAL PIECES   82

BIBLIOGRAPHY   89

The Making of Fine Glass

1: *Introduction*

THIS BOOK is intended for the layman, the student, the designer, or the critic who wishes to understand the fundamental processes of glassmaking. Needless to say, in this modern world where glass has been put to thousands of specialized uses it would be impossible to attempt in so small a work to describe in detail all the methods employed. This book intentionally limits itself to those basic processes which are common to all hand-glassmaking.

A knowledge of these processes will heighten the appreciation not only of modern glass but also of antique glass, for the methods described and illustrated here have remained essentially the same for two thousand years. So ancient and changeless is this craft that certain tools used by the modern glass blower still retain their Latin names.

It is a commonplace of aesthetics that a true appreciation of a work of art is impossible without at least a moderate understanding of the means by which it is produced. A person who could not distinguish between carved marble and cast bronze could scarcely be said to understand sculpture.

This principle of aesthetics is not to be considered an expression of snobbish and superficial "connoisseurship." Rather, it is the one basis of sound and deep appreciation for, without some knowledge of the basic potentialities and essential limitations of a given medium, it is impossible to understand either the artist's intention or to appreciate the fullness with which that intention has been achieved.

2: Design

IT IS OBVIOUS that sound design is the first essential of all art; but it is equally obvious that there will be a wide divergence of opinion as to what constitutes sound design. On one point alone would it be possible to find unanimity of opinion: that sound design is the full and true expression of the medium.

In the design of handmade glass, the limiting factors are numerous and dominating. The medium, during the time it is being worked, is hot, viscous, and heavy. It must be continually rotated to prevent its collapsing and must be kept at high temperature. At no time can the workman touch the object with his hands.

As a result of these simple factors, two corollaries of design result:

1. The objects produced must be round or must be the modification of round forms.

2. The size of the objects must be kept within strict limits.

It is true, for example, that a piece of handmade glass with any dimension exceeding eighteen inches is a *tour de force*.

These rudimentary examples will give some idea of limitations under which a designer of glass must work. Other limitations will be evident as we explore methods and processes more in detail.

Until very recently all glass was designed by the glassworkers themselves; new ideas were literally developed on the end of the blowing rod. Today the tendency is toward a separation between design and manufacture. The question of the comparative effectiveness of these approaches is too lengthy to be discussed here but, for the practical designer who is not a glass blower, a few suggestions may prove useful.

The drawing for a piece of glass should always be presented in straight elevation and at actual size. The glass blower sets his calipers directly from the drawing and he is greatly handicapped if it is necessary for him to work to scales.

In the designing of blown glass the making of preliminary models in other materials such as plaster or plasteline will, in general, be found more confusing than helpful. This is due to the fact that transparency and refraction are essential properties of glass which cannot be reproduced in opaque media. The best procedure, therefore, is to carry the design as far as possible on paper and then to correct it from actual samples in glass.

In general, the secondary forms of an object in glass should be somewhat heavier than in an opaque medium. Small forms tend to disappear because of transparency. For the same reason, all curves should be firm and robust. Because of the essential beauty of the material, glass, like silver or porcelain, is seen at its best when the forms are not over-elaborated.

It would be futile to attempt to lay down fixed rules of taste in glass. From year to year and from century to century styles and fashions in glass have changed, and so, presumably, they will continue to change. But it is safe to say that the present trend is away from the fragile forms best typified by Venetian glass and toward simpler and more robust expression.

One other factor of interest to the designer should be considered here: the question of color. Here again the matter of contemporary tendencies is involved. It is not an exaggeration to say that any color of the spectrum can be produced in glass. These colors can, furthermore, be used in various combinations in one piece of glass, as was the fashion during the early part of this century. But the present trend is overwhelmingly in the direction of colorless glass, a gratifying return to the true attributes of the medium, to the classic simplicity of pure crystal.

On the following pages will be found reproductions of typical working drawings for glass.

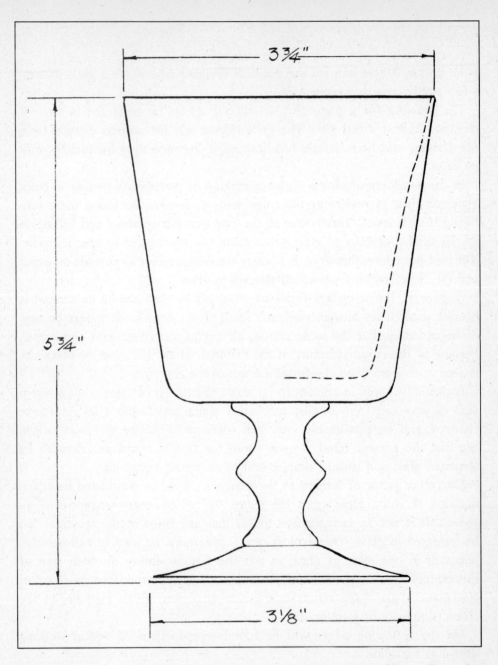

1: *Working drawing for goblet. The process of making this goblet is illustrated in Section 8.*

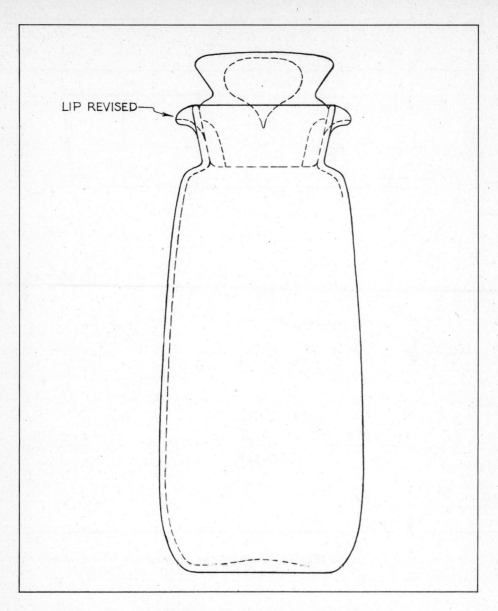

LIP REVISED

2: Working drawing for cocktail shaker.

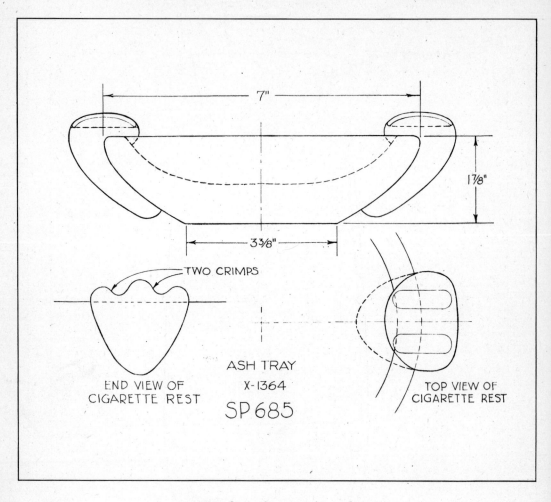

7"

1 7/8"

3 3/8"

TWO CRIMPS

END VIEW OF
CIGARETTE REST

ASH TRAY
X-1364
SP 685

TOP VIEW OF
CIGARETTE REST

3: Working drawing for ashtray.

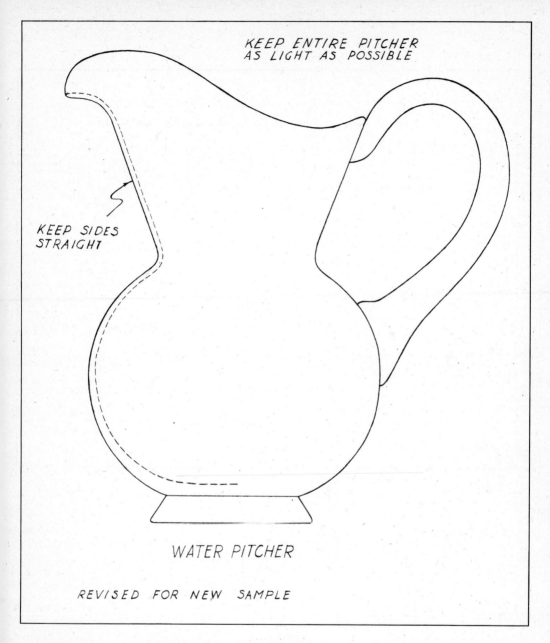

KEEP ENTIRE PITCHER
AS LIGHT AS POSSIBLE

KEEP SIDES
STRAIGHT

WATER PITCHER

REVISED FOR NEW SAMPLE

4: *Working drawing for pitcher. The making of the handle of the pitcher is illustrated in Section 10.*

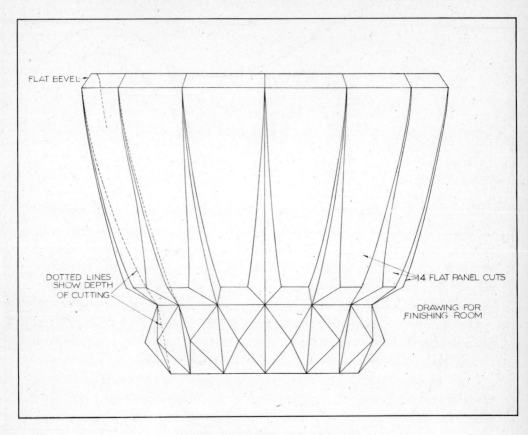

FLAT BEVEL

DOTTED LINES
SHOW DEPTH
OF CUTTING

14 FLAT PANEL CUTS

DRAWING FOR
FINISHING ROOM

5: Working drawing for a cut bowl.

3: *Material*

THE BASIC RAW MATERIAL from which all glass is made is silica, a constituent of sand. To the silica is added what is known as a "flux," which may be soda, potash, lime or lead in varying combinations, depending on the type of glass which is to be produced. The flux causes the sand to dissolve and fuse when subjected to high temperatures and imparts to the glass particular characteristics of weight, color and hardness.

Only the most practiced eye can distinguish between the many kinds of glass, old and new. But the average layman or student can quickly learn to recognize crystal glass, the composition with which we are here particularly concerned.

Let it be said at the outset that the term "crystal" is unfortunate in that it tends to create a confusion between natural rock crystal and crystal glass, two substances in no way related. The term "crystal" when applied to glass means simply a glass with a high lead content: 25% to 50% of the weight of the material. Lead is used in the form of litharge or lead monoxide and imparts certain definite characteristics to the glass. Crystal is noticeably more brilliant than other types of glass, it is appreciably heavier and, when struck, gives off a characteristic, bell-like ring. Though crystal may have color, the ideal toward which generations of glassmakers have striven is a colorless, transparent metal.

Color in glass is produced by the presence of metallic oxides. If a clear, colorless glass is desired, extraordinary precautions must be taken during the mixing and melting processes to assure absolute purity. The slightest trace of foreign matter will result in flaws and discoloration.

The commonest and most dangerous impurity is iron, the presence of which, even in the most minute quantity, will impart to the glass a greenish cast. To neutralize this greenish tinge, a "decolorizer," usually manganese, is sometimes added to the material before melting. But this method is unsatisfactory in that the resulting glass is dull and gray.

There is an old saying that "You cannot make a silk purse from a sow's ear," and in no craft is this more true than in the art of glassmaking. Without extreme purification of all the constituent materials and the greatest care in their mixing and melting, the true brilliance and purity of crystal can never be achieved.

4: On Blowing Glass

IT MUST BE EMPHASIZED that glass blowing, as described in these pages, is not within the scope of the amateur or of even the most talented artist or craftsman working alone. In the making of fine glass a multiplicity of tools and equipment is required. Furthermore, even such comparatively simple pieces as are here illustrated could not be produced without a number of artisans working together as a team.

It is the customary practice for glass blowers to work in groups of five to seven men, each with special functions and special manipulations to perform. Such a group, known as a "shop," has its own tools, equipment and reheating oven, and is under the direction of a highly skilled blower called a "gaffer." It is the gaffer who organizes and directs the work and performs the more difficult and delicate operations.

As will be seen in the following pages, a single piece of handmade glass is usually composed of several parts "gathered" from the furnace at different times and joined together at various stages of completion. Due to its high temperature in the working state, glass can be manipulated only for a very short time and, as the several parts must be joined at precisely the right moment and at just the proper heat, it is physically impossible for a man working alone to produce an object of any but the simplest character.

The tools and apparatus of the glass blower will be considered in detail as we proceed. In this highly skilled craft, years of apprenticeship are required before a blower is qualified to undertake the making of other than the simplest objects. Not only must the craftsman have extreme manual dexterity, but also an innate sense of temperature, volume and weight. Furthermore, he must possess that rare sense of form which will enable him to grasp the intention of design in many different styles and to execute them with accuracy, assurance, and speed. He must also have a natural feeling for teamwork—a quality conspicuously lacking in the generality of artists and artisans.

5: *Furnace and Shop Layout*

6: *The various constituents of glass are melted in clay crucibles (known as "pots") in large furnaces as illustrated above. Melting temperatures may be, for crystal, as high as 2500 degrees Fahrenheit.*

7: The gaffer's bench is the basic mechanical unit in the production of hand-made glass. By rolling the blowing iron back and forth along the projecting arms of the bench, the glass is caused to revolve while the gaffer works it with a variety of tools. This process and these tools are shown in more detail in subsequent illustrations.

At the right will be seen the small auxiliary furnace (known as the "glory-hole") where the glass is frequently reheated while being worked.

6: Tools

8: *Above is shown the wooden "forming-block" in which the gather of glass is rotated to form it into the shape of a ball and to give its surface a slightly harder consistency.*

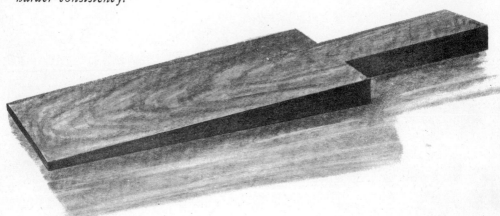

9: *The wooden paddle, or "pallet," is an important tool in glassmaking. It is used for the shaping of outer surfaces and for the truing of edges.*

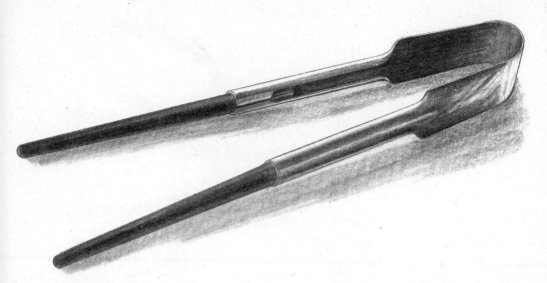

10: The "wood-jack" has a steel handle and wooden tips. It is used for the spreading of forms and for constriction in operations where no great pressure is required.

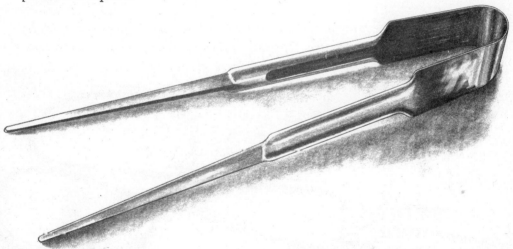

11: The "steel-jack" is used for constriction where pressure is required. The tips of this instrument have various sections—V-shaped, U-shaped, etc., depending on the form which is to be produced.

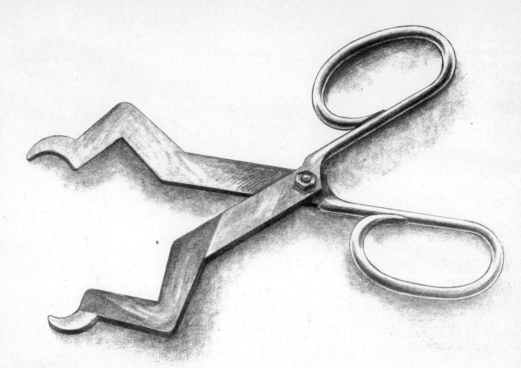

12: This tool is known as a "handle-shear." The outer prongs are used for grasping the blowing irons or "pontils" to guide them into correct position. The shear itself is used for cutting off large masses of hot glass.

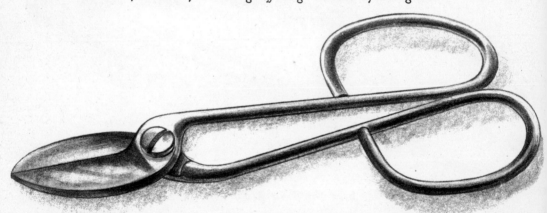

13: This type of shear is used for trimming excess glass from blown forms while the glass is still viscous.

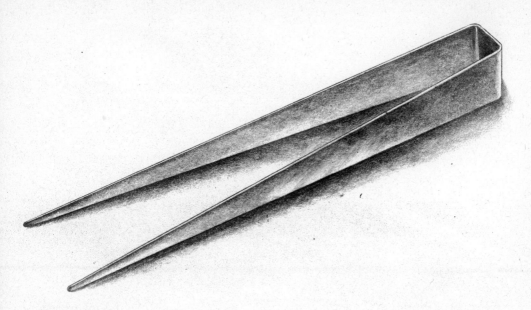

14: *The pincer is used for guiding the pontil into proper position and for the shaping of small forms.*

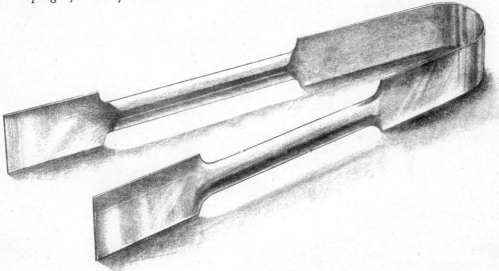

15: *The steel "forming-tool" is used for the aligning and shaping of "gafferea" forms.*

7: *Basic Manipulations*

CERTAIN MANIPULATIONS are fundamental in the making of all blown glass. All objects produced by the "off-hand" process must include, among many others, these basic processes.

16: First, a "gather" of molten glass is taken from the furnace by dipping the blowing iron into the molten metal.

17: *The gather is then rotated in a wooden forming block to give it uniformity of character.*

18: The glass is blown to form a bubble.

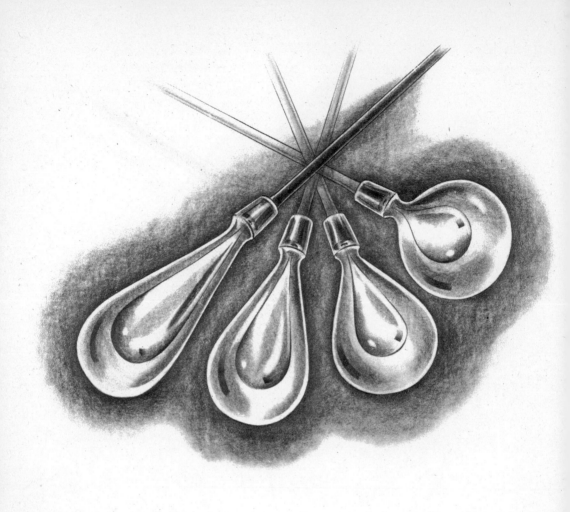

19: It may be elongated by swinging or flattened by spinning.

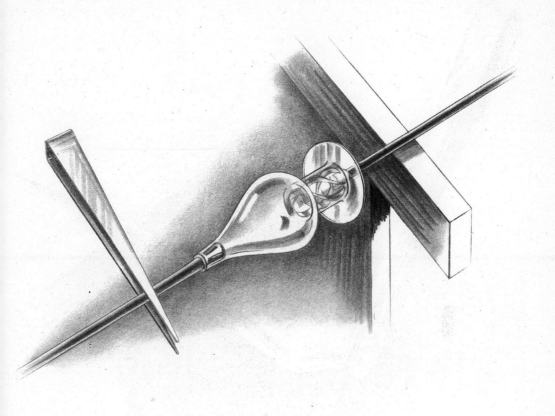

20: *While the glass is hot it may be combined with other elements.*

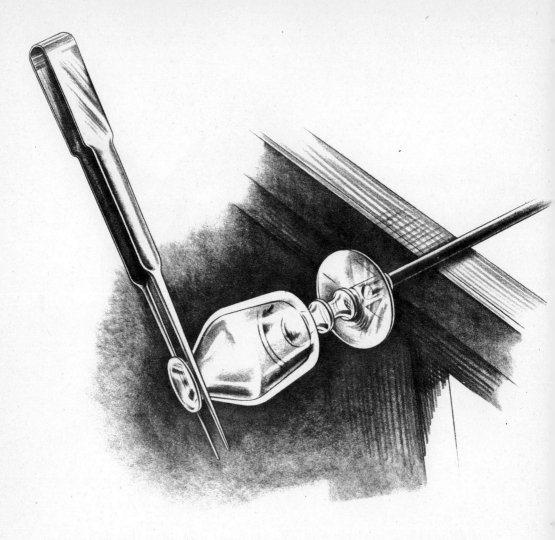

21: It can be constricted by the pressure of wooden or metal tools,

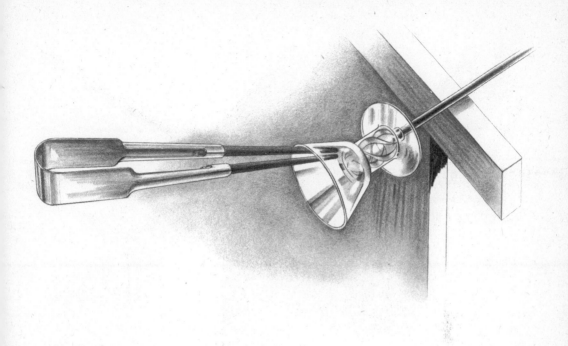

22: . . . or expanded by the use of the same instruments.

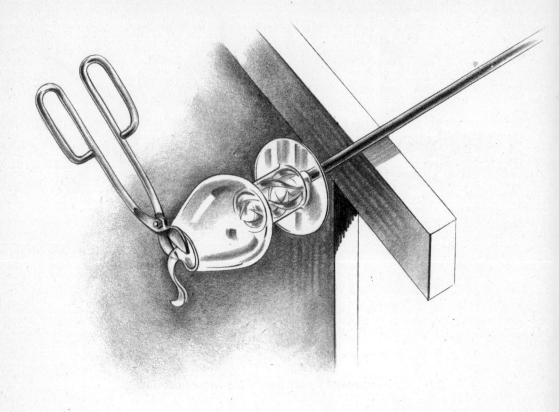

23: "Shearing," or cutting away excess glass gives the object its proper size.

24: *After a piece of glass has been shaped in the blowing room, it must go through a slow cooling process known as "annealing." This is necessary to prevent internal strains from being set up within the glass. It is effected by placing the object in a specially constructed oven, known as a "lehr," where it is carried on an endless belt through a series of slowly decreasing temperatures. The annealing of vases or table glass requires from five to eight hours.*

In the above illustration we see the tempered glass issuing from the lehr.

8: *Making a Goblet*

WE WILL HERE FOLLOW, step by step, the making of a goblet. This series of illustrations begins at the point where the glass has been gathered, unified in the forming-block, and the bubble blown. (See illustrations 16, 17, 18.)

25: A "gather of glass" is being "dropped" from the pontil. This mass is drawn out and cut off to the proper length to form the stem of the goblet. The shear holds the pontil in exact position.

26: The stem is tooled to its final shape with the steel-jack. During this and all other operations the piece is kept in rotation by rolling the iron back and forth on the arms of the bench.

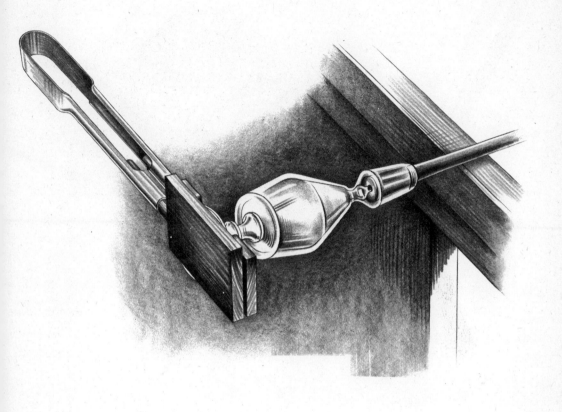

27: *Another gather of glass has been dropped onto the stem and is here being shaped into the foot with a special forming tool.*

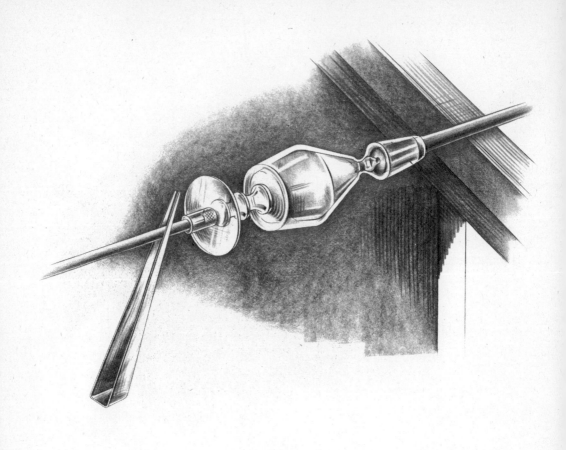

28: *A pontil is attached to the foot, guided into position with a pincer.*

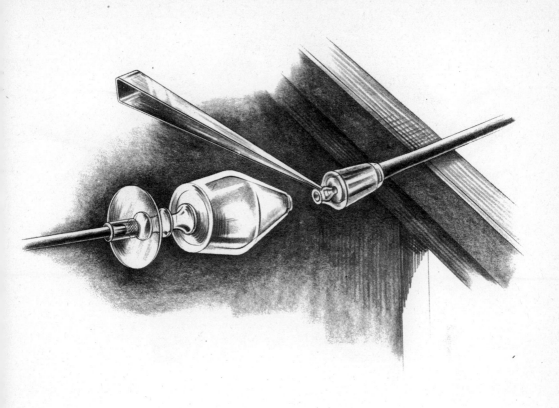

29: *The goblet is cracked off from the blowing iron with a touch of a cold pincer.*

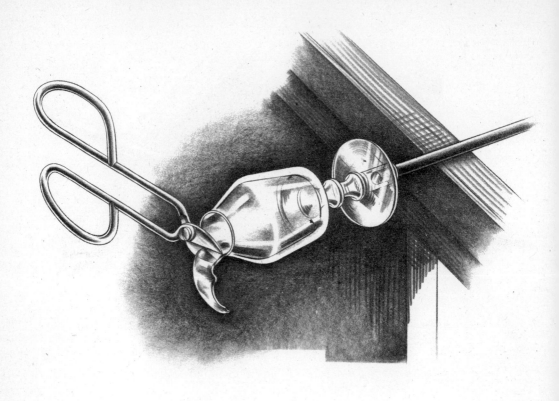

30: *The piece is now reversed on the arms of the bench and the excess glass is sheared off.*

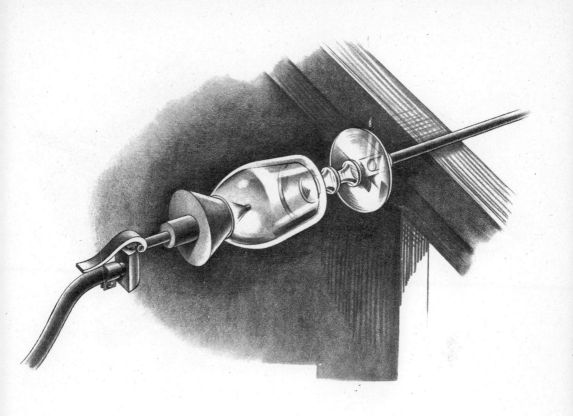

31: A puff of compressed air expands the bowl of the goblet to its proper size.

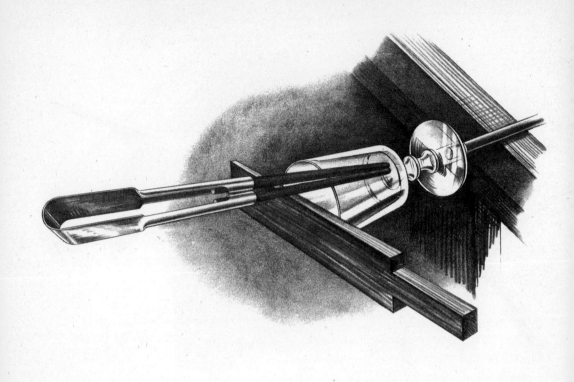

32: *The bowl of the goblet is then opened out and brought to its final shape with the wood-jack, while the rim is kept true by the pressure of a pallet held by an assistant. The blowing of the goblet is now complete and it will be carried to the lehr for annealing.*

9: *Making a Decorative Bowl*

WE WILL HERE FOLLOW, step by step, the making of a more complex piece: a large bowl, the base of which is elaborated by a typical technique of glass blowing—the trapping of air bubbles within the glass to form a geometric pattern. This is done to add brilliance to the glass and may be used in a variety of ways to produce definite aesthetic effects. It is not to be confused with accidental bubbles which occur in glass as the result of impure ingredients or faulty workmanship. On the contrary, as will be seen, it is a carefully controlled and difficult technique.

This series of illustrations begins at the point where the glass has been gathered, unified in the forming block, and the bubble blown. (See illustrations 16, 17, 18.)

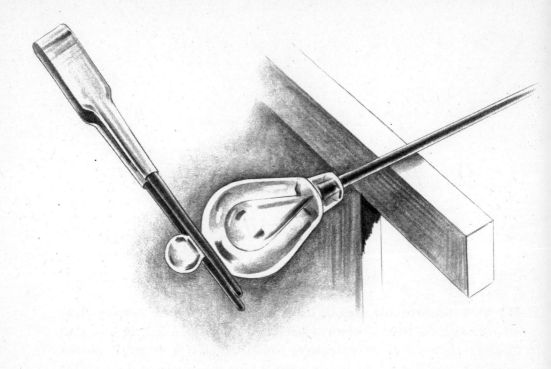

33: *By constriction with a wood-jack a ball is formed at the end of the bubble, which is continually being rotated by rolling the blowing iron on the arms of the bench. This is the first step in forming the base of the bowl.*

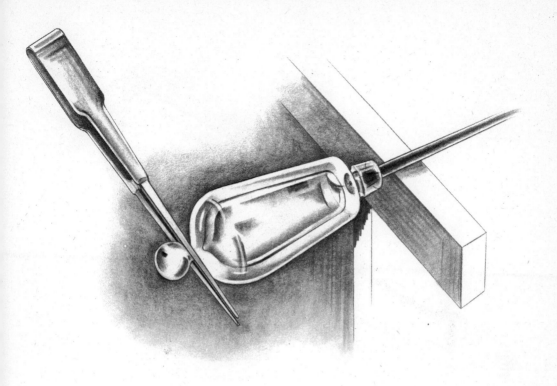

34: A pulling action with a steel-jack elongates the bubble.

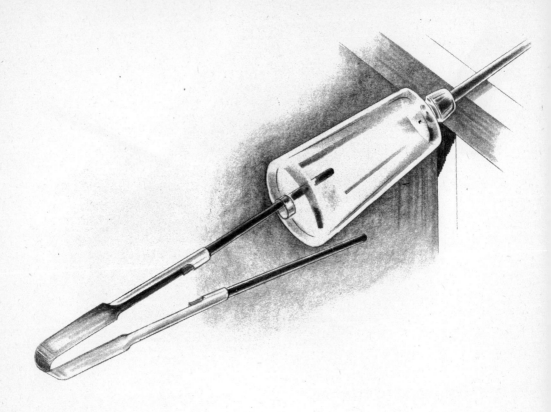

35: The ball is knocked off and the resulting hole is opened out with the wood-jack.

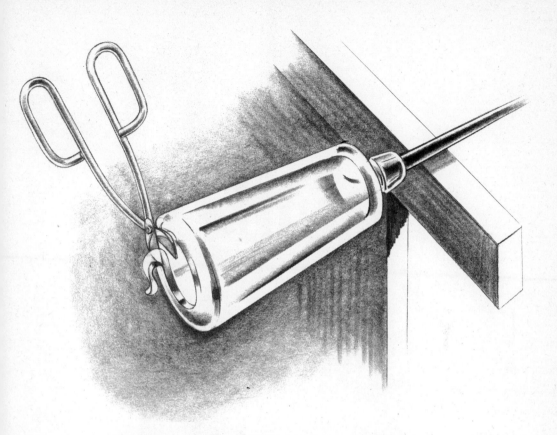

36: The hole is sheared open to form a cylindrical cup.

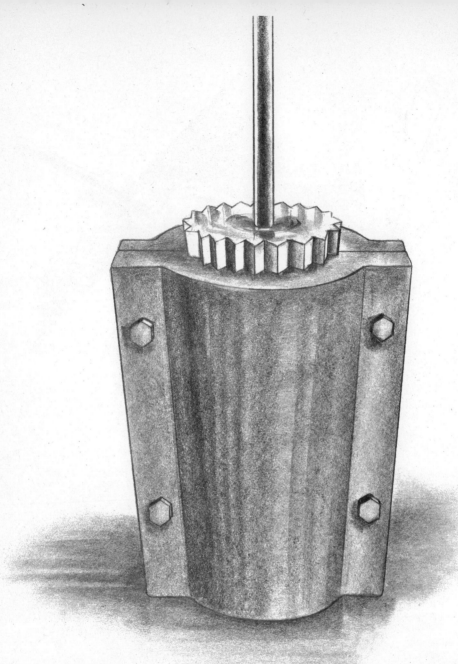

37: *While the previous manipulations are carried out, another gather of glass is plunged into a corrugated mould, known as a "crimp" mould, and allowed to cool slightly.*

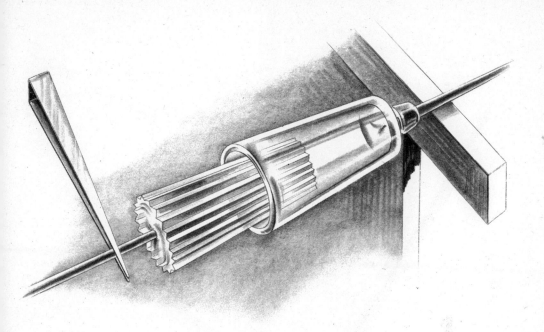

38: This second element is inserted in the cylindrical cup shown in illustration 36. The glass is then carefully broken away from the pontil-rod (at left) and remains attached to the blowing iron.

39: *The glass is reheated and rolled on a steel table. This process is called "marvering." It unifies the glass but, at the same time, the air that was trapped in the grooves seen in illustration 38 has formed longitudinal bubbles, evenly spaced within the outer shell of the cylinder.*

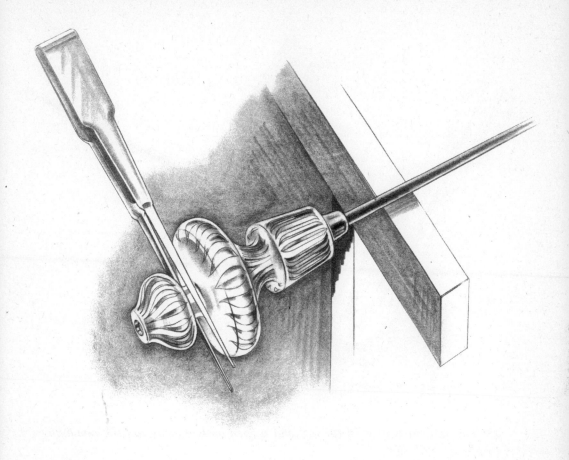

40: *The glass cylinder is tooled to the desired shape by constriction with a V-shaped steel-jack.*

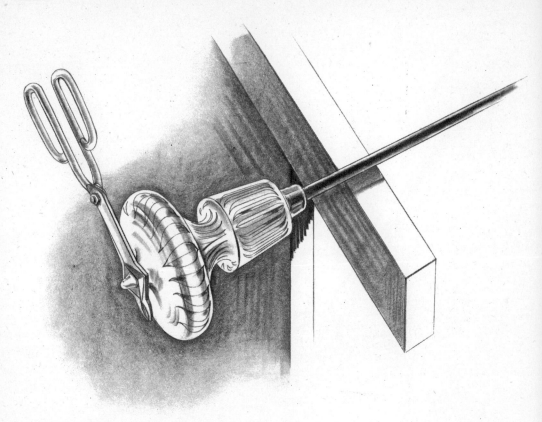

41: *The bulbous section of the left end is then broken away and the remaining stem is sheared off.*

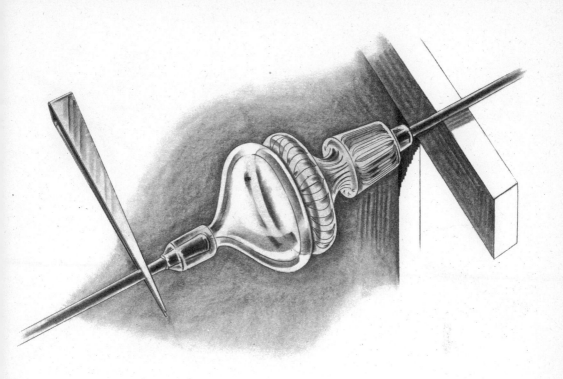

42: In the meantime, another gather of glass has been taken from the furnace and blown to form a bubble of the desired size to form the base of the bowl. The bubble is here being applied to the element shown in illustration 41. The two parts adhere and solidify automatically.

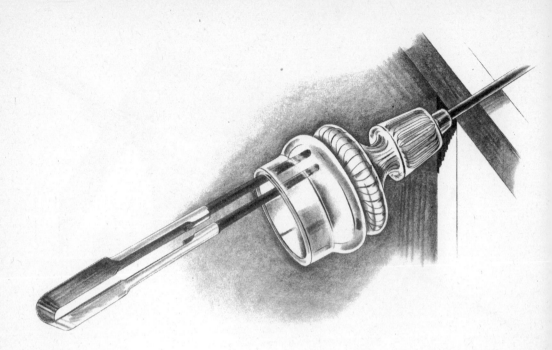

43: The blowing iron seen at the left in illustration 42 is then knocked off, and the bulb is opened out with a wood-jack.

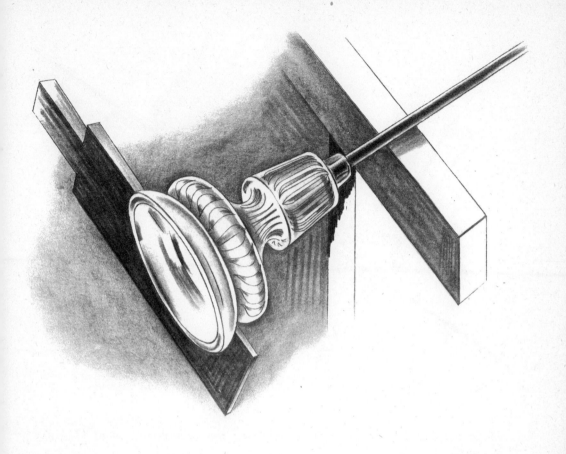

44: *The glass is tooled with a wooden paddle to the desired shape.*

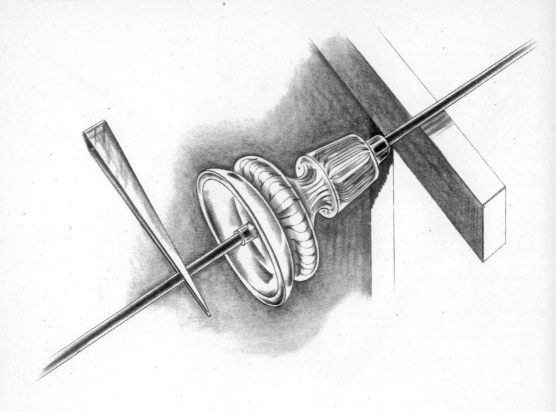

45: *A pontil-rod is attached to the base, and the bulbous section of glass at the right is cut away.*

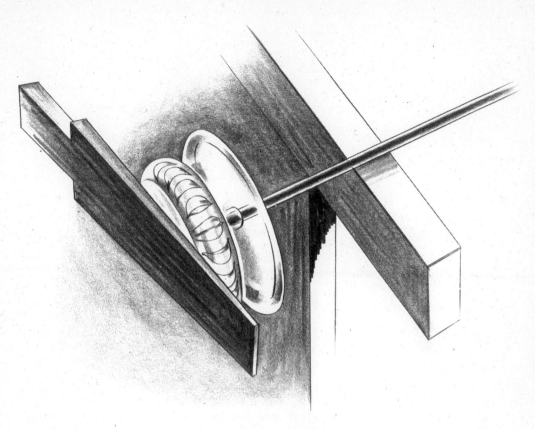

46: *The piece is now reversed on the arms of the blowers bench and the remaining mass, containing air bubbles in a geometric pattern, is smoothed with a wooden paddle. The base is now completed.*

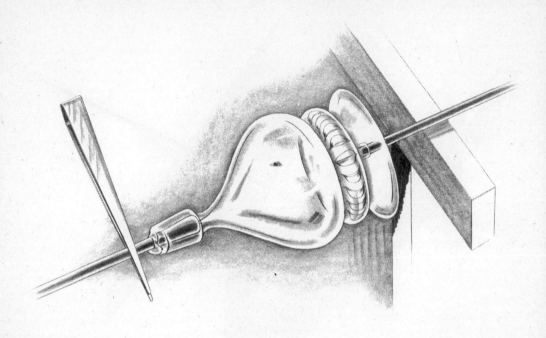

47: *In the meantime, still another bulb has been blown and is applied to the base. This bulb will form the main part of the bowl.*

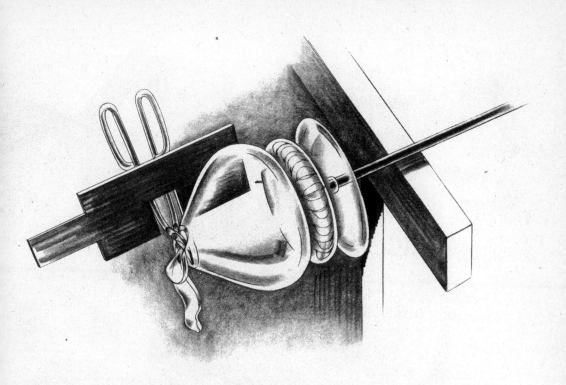

48: *The blowing iron seen at the left in illustration 47 is knocked off and the excess glass is cut away. The paddle at the left in this drawing is held by an assistant and protects the blower's hand from the radiant heat of the glass during the shearing process.*

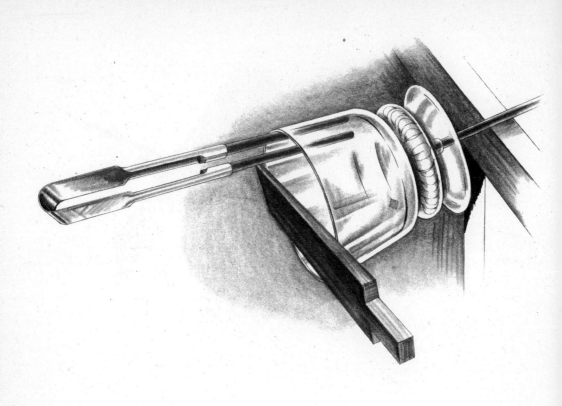

49: *The bowl is opened with a wood-jack while the assistant holds the wooden paddle against the edge of the bowl to keep it true. During all these processes the bowl is continually rotated by rolling it back and forth on the arms of the bench.*

50: *The completed piece is held in an upright position and the pontil-rod (at bottom) is knocked off by a sharp blow of a tool (at lower right), and is picked up on a long stick with an asbestos covered prong (at right). The bowl is then carried to the kiln or lehr for cooling.*

10: *Gaffered Forms*

MASSES OF GLASS which are added to a piece during the process of blowing are known as "gaffered" forms. These elements, such as handles and bases, become an integral part of the object and are typical of handmade glass.

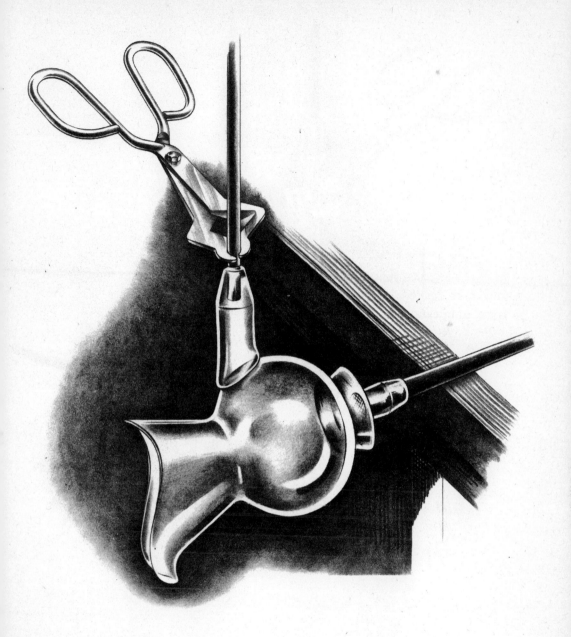

51: *Here a gather is being dropped on to form a handle.*

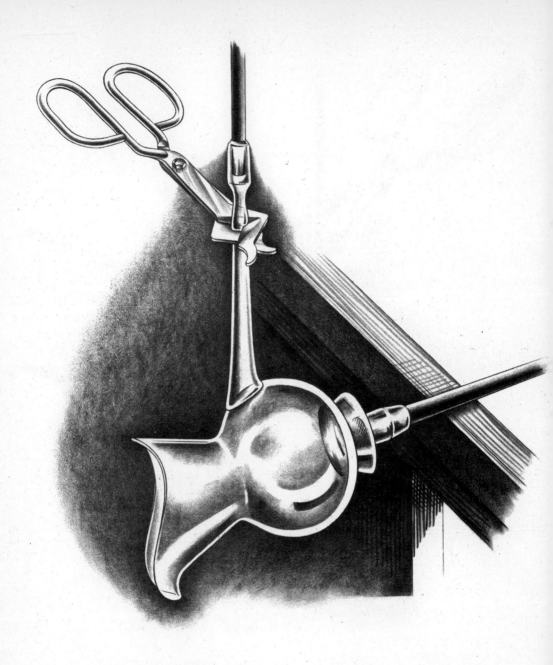

52: *The glass is drawn out to the proper length and sheared off.*

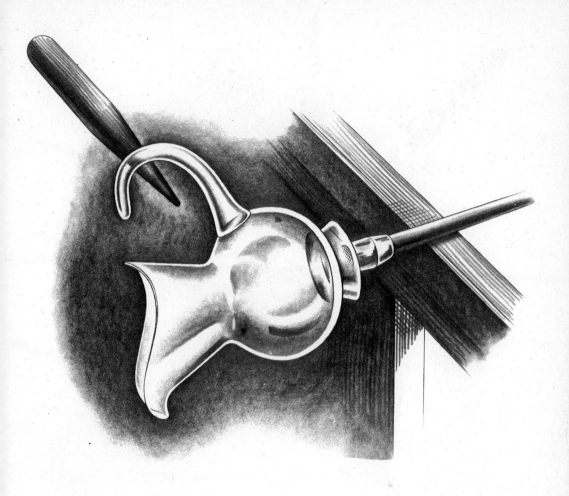

53: By use of various tools the glass is shaped into the desired form.

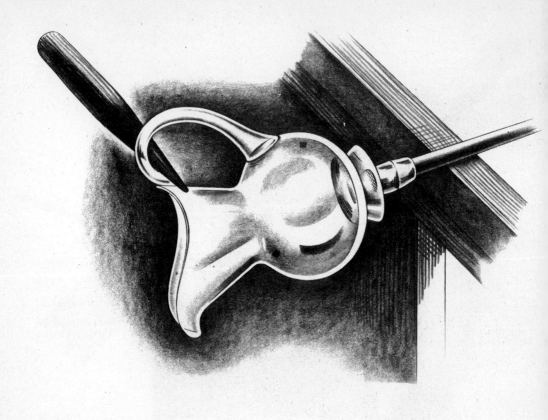

54: We see here the completed form.

11: *Cutting*

THE ANCIENT ART of cutting glass by the use of stone wheels was perfected by English glassmakers during the Eighteenth Century. Later extensively imitated in cheap and over-elaborated patterns produced by the use of moulds, cut glass has fallen into an unmerited disrepute and is sometimes considered synonymous with false elegance. Even though present day taste may tend toward the simple and the un-ornate, fine cut glass such as Waterford will remain an expression of intrinsic and special beauty.

Two definite tendencies may be noted in the design of cut glass: the first, by surface cutting, aims to add brilliance to the crystal; the second, by grinding away large masses of glass, attempts to create new forms. While the latter trend is the more modern, it does not necessarily follow that it is the more correct.

In either case, the essential operations and the tools employed are the same. The piece which is to be cut is first blown and annealed by the processes which we have observed.

55: *The forms to be cut are laid out in ink on the surface of the glass with a small brush.*

56: *These forms are cut by slowly revolving wheels of sandstone or carborundum, varying in diameter from three to eighteen inches.*

57: *The abrasive action of the cutting wheels leaves on the glass a rough, white surface, which is polished away by felt wheels fed with putty powder, thus restoring the transparency and clarity of the glass.*

12: *Engraving*

COPPER WHEEL ENGRAVING is one of the rarest and most difficult of handicrafts. By this process designs of almost any character can be engraved on the surface of glass objects. At its best, copper wheel engraving equals in quality the work of the most accomplished medalists and exhibits that combination of delicacy and precision of form which is associated with classic gems and cameos.

The process is so extremely difficult that perfection is rarely attained. Not only are years of apprenticeship and experience required, but also the engraver must have the understanding of form of a sculptor, the instincts of a mechanic and the patience of Job. Furthermore, he must have that innate sense of style which is the first qualification of the interpretive artist. Like the violinist or the pianist he must be able to bring to its final expression the work of many men whose approach to design and whose sense of form is utterly different. For example, one of the few outstanding engravers in America has successfully interpreted in glass the work of more than thirty famous artists, with styles as diverse as those of Manship and Matisse.

The glass engraver works from a drawing and must have infinite sensitivity and skill to transform the design into the medium of glass.

58: *The engraver works at a small lathe into which are fitted, one at a time, scores of interchangeable copper wheels.*

59: *The glass is pressed upward against the wheel, which is fed by an abrasive of linseed oil and emery powder. The result is a shallow intaglio which, by an optical illusion, appears to the eye as a bas-relief.*

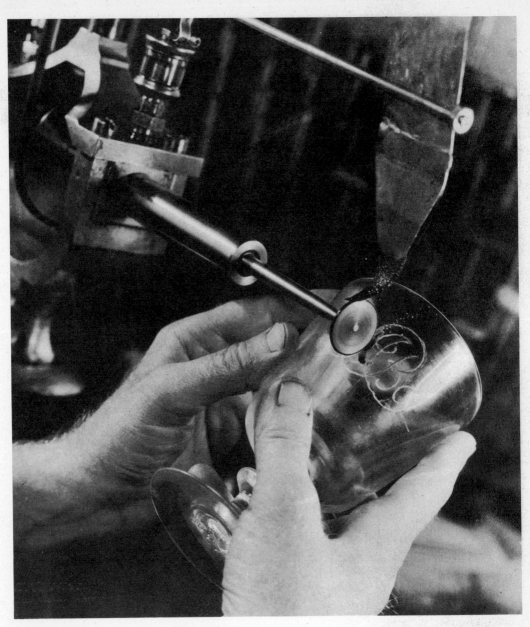

60: Fine monogramming is also carried out by copper wheel engraving. This exquisite work can be distinguished from the less finished effects of sandblasting and acid etching by the firmness of its forms and the sharpness of its edges.

61: *The wheels used in this process are thin sheets of copper, and vary in diameter from one eighth of an inch to four inches. The engraver must use great judgement in choosing the proper wheel to produce a given form. In carrying out even a simple design, as many as fifty different wheels may be used.*

13: *Typical Pieces*

A SOUND UNDERSTANDING of fine glass can be achieved only by study of the best examples of the art. Such examples will be found in all the larger museums or may be studied to almost equal advantage in the many books and pamphlets on glass.

A careful examination of the great glass of all periods is essential to the critic and the connoisseur. From the works of the past and the present the designer will learn not only what is natural to the medium, but also many things which should be avoided. The making of glass involves many complex techniques and a careful study of all available source material is the only "short-cut" to effective design and the only basis of sound appreciation.

For those to whom museums and reference works are not available, the following illustrations may be of some slight assistance toward a better understanding of the methods and processes described in other sections of this book.

62: This cocktail shaker is an excellent example of a simple blown form.

63: *A complete place-setting of crystal, showing typical blown forms with engraved monograms.*

64: Bowl with gaffered decoration on base.

65: *This bowl is cut with stone wheels from a piece originally round.*

66: A fine example of a blown piece with gaffered handles and engraved coat of arms.

67: *A successful combination of a blown bowl, engraved decoration and a cut base.*

Bibliography

Introductory Note

The following list of books constitutes a basic bibliography for the student and lover of fine glass. An arbitrary classification of the titles has been made in order to group together, as far as possible, books on similar subjects.

Each title listed is considered important, but there are several of particular interest. THE ART OF GLASS by Antonio Neri (translated by Christopher Merret of London in 1662) is the first known book devoted entirely to the subject of glass. It was written by an Italian priest, published in Florence in 1612, and later translated from the Italian by Christopher Merret.

CURIOSITIES OF GLASSMAKING by Apsley Pellatt, published in 1849, is the result of research for information in the works of Neri, Merret, Kunckel, Blancourt and others. It is a book of great charm and supplies many interesting facts on the chemistry of color in glass, as well as the modes of glass blowing, shaping, or moulding in the ancient world, the Middle Ages, and up to the date of publication.

Other titles worthy of mention are: DE L'ART DE LA VERRERIE by Jean Haudicquer de Blancourt, OLD ENGLISH GLASSES by Albert Hartshorne, DAS GLAS IM ALTERTUME by Anton Kisa, RARE ENGLISH GLASSES OF THE XVII and XVIII CENTURIES by Joseph Bles, and STIEGEL GLASS by Frederick William Hunter.

An especially good source on English Glass is a volume entitled ENGLISH GLASS by W. A. Thorpe, a contemporary authority on the subject.

Not nearly enough has been written on American Glass. Probably the best known writers on the subject are Ruth Webb Lee and George and Helen McKearin. Modern glass, too, has been neglected. The two most popular books are Guillaume Janneau's MODERN GLASS and MODERN FINE GLASS by Leloise Skelley.

General Works on Glass

BUCKLEY, Wilfred. The Art of Glass, Illustrated from the Wilfred Buckley Collection in the Victoria and Albert Museum, London. (Illustrated with 181 plates.) New York, The Phaidon Press, 1939. 11¾ x 8½ inches, pp. 286.

DILLON, Edward. Glass. (Illustrated with 49 plates some of which are in color.) London, Methuen and Company, 1907. 10 x 7 inches, pp. 374, indexed.

EISEN, Gustavus A. Glass. Its Origin, History, Chronology, Technic, and Classification to the Sixteenth Century. (Illustrated with 198 plates and 284 figures.) New York, W. E. Rudge, 1927. 2 volumes, 10 x 7½ inches, pp. 769, indexed.

METROPOLITAN MUSEUM OF ART. A Special Exhibition of Glass from the Museum Collections. (Illustrated with 42 plates.) New York, Metropolitan Museum of Art, 1936. 8⅝ x 5½ inches, pp. 45.

MOORE, N. Hudson. Old Glass, European and American. (With 265 illustrations.) New York, Frederick A. Stokes, 1924. 9½ x 6½ inches, pp. 394, indexed.

PERRY, Josephine. The Glass Industry. (Illustrated.) New York and Toronto, Longmans, Green & Company, 1945. 8¼ x 6¼ inches, pp. 128, indexed.

ROGERS, Frances, and BEARD, Alice. 5000 Years of Glass. (Illustrated with line drawings throughout the text by authors and 8 half-tones from photographs.) New York, Frederick A. Stokes, 1937. 8¼ x 5¾ inches, pp. 303, indexed.

SKELLEY, Leloise Davis. Modern Fine Glass. (Illustrated with 90 photographs.) New York, Richard R. Smith, 1937. 12½ x 9½ inches, pp. 144, indexed.

Ancient Glass

DEVILLE, Achille. Histoire de l'Art de la Verrerie dans l'Antiquité. (Illustrated with 112 plates.) Paris, Morel, 1873. 13 x 9½ inches, pp. 108, indexed.

KISA, Anton. Das Glas im Altertume. (Illustrated with 414 drawings and photographs.) Leipzig, Karl W. Hiersemann, 1908. 3 volumes, 9¼ x 6½ inches, pp. 978, indexed.

LAMM, Carl J. Oriental Glass of Mediaeval Date Found in Sweden, and the Early History of Lustre-Painting. (Illustrated with 24 plates of photographs.) Stockholm, Wahlström & Widstrand, 1941. 9⅝ x 6⅝ inches, pp. 114, indexed.

BATE, Percy. English Table Glass. (Illustrated with 67 plates.) London, B. T. Batsford, 1913. 9 x 5½ inches, pp. 130, indexed.

BLES, Joseph. Rare English Glasses of the XVII & XVIII Centuries. (Illustrated with 100 plates showing 147 pieces.) New York and Boston, Houghton Mifflin Company, 1925. 12¾ x 10½ inches, pp. 269.

BUCKLEY, Francis. English Baluster Stemmed Glasses of Seventeenth and Eighteenth Centuries. (Illustrated with 18 plates black and white drawings.) Edinburgh, Privately printed at the Ballantyne Press, 1912. 12¾ x 10¼ inches, pp. 29.

BUCKLEY, Francis. A History of Old English Glass. (Illustrated with 60 plates.) London, Ernest Benn, Ltd., 1925. 11 x 9 inches, pp. 155, indexed.

FLEMING, Arnold. Scottish and Jacobite Glass. (Illustrated with 56 plates.) Glasgow, Jackson, Son and Company, 1938. 11¼ x 8¾ inches, pp. 196, indexed.

FRANCIS, Grant R. Old English Drinking Glasses. Their Chronology and Sequence. (Illustrated with 385 drinking glasses and 8 special plates.) London, Herbert Jenkins, Ltd., 1926. 12¾ x 10½ inches, pp. 222, indexed.

HARTSHORNE, Albert. Old English Glasses. An Account of Glass Drinking Vessels in England from Early Times to the End of the 18th Century. With introductory notices, original documents, etc. (Illustrated with 366 textual figures and 67 plates.) London, Edward Arnold, 1897. 13¼ x 10¼ inches, pp. 490, indexed.

HONEY, W. B. Glass. A Handbook for the Study of Glass Vessels of All Periods and Countries and A Guide to the Museum Collection. (Illustrated with 70 photographs.) London, Published under the Authority of the Ministry of Education, 1946. 10 x 7⅜ inches, pp. 169, indexed.

HONEY, W. B. English Glass. (Illustrated with 8 plates in color and 26 illustrations in black and white.) London, Collins, 1946. 9 x 6½ inches, pp. 47.

LEWIS, J. Sidney. Old Glass and How to Collect It. (Illustrated with 60 plates.) London, Werner Laurie, Ltd., 1928. 8¾ x 7 inches, pp. 258.

PERCIVAL, MacIver. The Glass Collector. A Guide to Old English Glass. (Illustrated with 30 plates and textual drawings.) London, Jenkins, n.d. 7½ x 5 inches, pp. 331, indexed.

BUCKLEY, Wilfred. European Glass. A Brief Outline of the History of Glass Making . . ., Illustrated by Examples in the Collection of the Author. With a foreword by Bernard Rackham, and an Essay on Dutch Engraving by Dr. Ferrand Hudig. (Illustrated with 110 plates.) New York and Boston, Houghton Mifflin Company, 1926. 11¼ x 9 inches, pp. 96.

BUCKLEY, Wilfred. Notes on Franz Greenwood and the Glasses that He Engraved. (Illustrated with 36 plates.) London, Ernest Benn, Ltd., 1930. 11½ x 8¾ inches, pp. 14.

CHAVANCE, René. La Céramique et la Verrerie. (Illustrated with 24 plates.) Paris, Rieder, 1928. 8 x 5¼ inches, pp. 133.

FROTHINGHAM, Alice Wilson. Hispanic Glass. With Examples in the Collection of the Hispanic Society of America. (With 125 illustrations.) New York, The Hispanic Society of America. 1941. 9 x 6 inches, pp. 204, indexed.

JANNEAU, Guillaume. Modern Glass. (Illustrated with numerous photographs.) New York, Wm. Edwin Rudge, 1931. 11½ x 9 inches, pp. 184, index to illustrations.

JANNEAU, Guillaume. Le Verre et l'Art de Marinot. (Illustrated with line drawings.) Paris, H. Floury, 1925. 9⅝ x 7½ inches, pp. 79.

PAZAUREK, Gustav E. Moderne Gläser. (Illustrated with textual drawings and photographs.) Leipzig, Hermann Seemann Nachfolger, n.d. 10¼ x 7½ inches, pp. 133.

PELLIOT, Marianne. Verres Anciens. (With 48 illustrated plates.) Paris & Bruxelles, Van Oest, 1929. 13 x 10 inches, pp. 153.

POWELL, Harry J. Glass-Making in England. (With 106 textual illustrations.) Cambridge, Cambridge University Press, 1923. 11 x 7½ inches, pp. 183, indexed.

ROSENTHAL, Leon. La Verrerie Française depuis Cinquante Ans. (Illustrated with 32 plates.) Paris and Bruxelles, Van Oest, 1927. 8½ x 6½ inches, pp. 47.

SCHMIDT, Robert. Das Glas. (Illustrated with textual drawings.) Berlin and Leipzig, Walter De Gruyter & Co., 1922. 8 x 5½ inches, pp. 419, indexed.

STROMBERG, Edv. (and others). Modernt Svenskt Glas. Utveckling. Teknik. Form. (Illustrated with textual photographs and line drawings.) Stockholm, Jonson & Winter, 1943. 11¼ x 7½ inches, pp. 254.

THORPE, W. A. English Glass. (With 24 pages of illustrations from photographs and 30 textual figures.) London, A. & C. Black, Ltd., 1935. 8½ x 5½ inches, pp. 301, indexed.

THORPE, W. A. A History of English and Irish Glass. (Illustrated with 168 plates and 35 textual figures.) London, The Medici Society, 1929. 2 volumes, 10½ x 8 inches, pp. 372, indexed.

WESTROPP, M. S. Dudley. Irish Glass. An Account of Glass Making in Ireland from the XVI Century to the Present Day. (Illustrated with reproductions of 188 typical pieces of Irish glass and 220 patterns and designs.) London, Herbert Jenkins, Ltd., (1920). 11 x 8½ inches, pp. 206, indexed.

YOXALL, J. H. Collecting Old Glass, English and Irish. (Numerous illustrations.) London, W. Heinemann, 1916. 7 x 4¼ inches, pp. 109, indexed.

European and Oriental Glass

BUCKLEY, Wilfred. Aert Schouman and the Glasses that He Engraved. With a Supplementary Note on Glasses Engraved by Frans Greenwood. (Illustrated with 30 plates.) London, Ernest Benn, Ltd., 1931. 11½ x 8¾ inches, pp. 50.

BUCKLEY, Wilfred. D. Wolff and the Glasses that He Engraved. With a Supplementary Note on a Glass Engraved by Frans Greenwood. (Illustrated with 25 plates.) London, Methuen & Company, Ltd., 1935. 11½ x 8½ inches, pp. 41.

BUCKLEY, Wilfred. Diamond Engraved Glasses of the Sixteenth Century. With Particular Reference to Five Attributed to Giacomo Verselini. (Illustrated with 33 plates.) London, Ernest Benn, Ltd., 1929. 11½ x 8¾ inches, pp. 24.

SEITZ, Heribert. Äldre Svenska Glas med Graverad Dekor. En Undersökning av det Bevarade 1700-talsbeståndet. With an English summary. (Illustrated with 75 plates and textual drawings.) Stockholm, 1936. 11¼ x 7½ inches, pp. 231, indexed.

SEITZ, Heribert. Glaset Förr och Nu. (Illustrated with 117 plates and drawings in the text.) Stockholm, Albert Bonniers, 1933. 10¼ x 7 inches, pp. 160, indexed.

WETTERGREN, Erik. Moderne Schwedische Werkkunst. (Illustrated with numerous photographic plates and textual photographs.) Malmö, 1926. 11¾ x 8¾ inches, pp. 206.

WETTERGREN, Erik. Orreforsglas. (With numerous illustrations.) ·Stockholm, Gunnar Tisells, 1921. 12½ x 9½ inches, pp. 32.

American Glass

BARBER, Edwin Atlee. American Glassware Old and New. A Sketch of the Glass Industry in the United States and Manual for Collectors of Historical Bottles. (Illustrated with photographs and line drawings.) Philadelphia, David McKay, 1900. 7 x 5 inches, pp. 112, indexed.

BROOKLYN MUSEUM, Department of Industrial Art. Handbook of American Glass Industries. (Illustrated with Photographs.) Brooklyn, Brooklyn Museum Press, 1936. 8½ x 5¾ inches, pp. 117.

HULL, Maude Pollard. Early Glass-Making in Virginia. Richmond, Published by Author, 1933. 9 x 6 inches, pp. 22.

HUNTER, Frederick William. Stiegel Glass. (Illustrated with 12 plates in color from autochromes by J. B. Kerfoot and 159 half-tones.) Boston, Houghton Mifflin, 1914. 10¼ x 7¼ inches, pp. 272, indexed.

IRWIN, Frederick T. The Story of Sandwich Glass and Glass Workers. (Illustrated with textual drawings and plates.) Manchester, N. H., Privately printed, 1926. 8¾ x 5½ inches, pp. 99.

KNITTLE, Rhea Mansfield. Early American Glass. (Illustrated with 64 plates.) New York, The Century Company, 1927. 8¼ x 5⅝ inches, pp. 496, indexed.

LEE, Ruth Webb. Antique Fakes and Reproductions. (Illustrated with 101 plates of photographs.) Framingham Centre, Mass., Published by Author, 1938. 8¾ x 5⅝ inches, pp. 224, indexed.

LEE, Ruth Webb. Early American Pressed Glass. A Classification of Patterns Collectible in Sets together with Individual Pieces for Table Decorations. (With 190 illustrations.) Pittsford, N. Y., Published by Author, 1933. 8¾ x 6 inches, pp. 683, indexed.

LEE, Ruth Webb. Ruth Webb Lee's Handbook of Early American Pressed Glass Patterns. (Illustrated with 190 plates of photographs and drawings.) Northboro, Mass., Published by Author, 1936. 8 x 5¼ inches, indexed.

LEE, Ruth Webb. Sandwich Glass. The History of the Boston and Sandwich Glass Company. (Illustrated with 203 plates.) Framingham Centre, Mass., Published by Author, 1939. 8¾ x 5⅝ inches, pp. 526, indexed.

LEE, Ruth Webb. Victorian Glass. Specialties of the 19th Century. (Illustrated with 60 plates.) Northboro, Mass., Published by Author, 1944. 8¾ x 5½ inches, pp. 608.

McKEARIN, George S. and Helen. American Glass. (Illustrated with 2000 plates of photographs and 1000 drawings by James L. McCreery.) New York, Crown Publishers, 1941. 10¾ x 8 inches, pp. 622, indexed.

NORTHEND, Mary Harrod. American Glass. (With 70 illustrations.) New York, Tudor Publishing Co., 1936. 9¼ x 6 inches, pp. 209.

SMITH, Francis Edgar. American Glass Paperweights. (Illustrated with 30 plates.) Wollaston, Mass., Antique Press, 1939. 7¼ x 5 inches, pp. 173.

VAN RENSSELAER, Stephen. Early American Bottles and Flasks. (Illustrated with drawings and photographs.) Peterborough, N. H., Transcript Printing Company, 1936. 9¼ x 6⅛ inches, pp. 320.

WALBRIDGE, William S. American Bottles Old and New. A Story of the Industry in the United States. (Illustrated with textual photographs.) Toledo, O., Owens Bottle Company, 1920. 8¼ x 6¼ inches, pp. 112.

WATKINS, Lura Woodside. Cambridge Glass, 1818 to 1888. (Illustrated with 80 plates.) Boston, Marshall Jones Company, 1930. 8 x 5½ inches, pp. 199, indexed.

Special Glass Subjects

BERGSTROM, Evangeline H. Old Glass Paperweights. (Illustrated with colored and uncolored photographs.) Chicago, Ill., Lakeside Press, 1940. 9¼ x 6¼ inches, pp. 120, with a glossary of terms.

DUTHIE, Arthur Louis. Decorative Glass Processes. (Illustrated with textual drawings and photographs.) London, Archibald Constable & Co., Ltd., 1908. 8½ x 5¾ inches, pp. 267, indexed.

MONSON-FITZJOHN, G. J. Drinking Vessels of Bygone Days, from the Neolithic Age to the Georgian Period. (Illustrated with drawings in the text by Harry Howard . . . and others.) London, Jenkins, 1927. 8½ x 7 inches, pp. 144, indexed.

SILVERMAN, Alexander. Frederick Carder, Artist and Glass Technologist. Columbus, Ohio, From the Bulletin of the American Ceramic Society, Sept. 1939. 10½ x 7¾ inches, pp. 8.

HAUDICQUER De Blancourt, J. De l'Art de la Verrerie. (Illustrated.) Paris, Jean Jombert, 1697. 6¾ x 4 inches, pp. 607.

JARVES, Deming. Reminiscences of Glass-Making. (Illustrated with 4 plates of drawings.) New York, Hurd & Houghton, 1865. 7¾ x 5¼ inches, pp. 116.

LARDNER, Dionysius. A Treatise on the Origin, Progressive Improvement, and Present State of the Manufacture of Porcelain and Glass. (Illustrated with cuts throughout the text.) London, Longman, Rees, etc. 1832. 7 x 4¼ inches, pp. 334, indexed.

NERI, Antonio. The Art of Glass . . . translated by C(hristopher) M(erret) London, A. W. for Octavian Pulleyn, 1662. 7 x 4 inches, pp. 362.

PELLATT, Apsley, Curiosities of Glass Making: with Details of the Process and Productions of Ancient and Modern Ornamental Glass Manufacture. (Illustrated with drawings and photographs.) London, David Bogue, 1849. 8¾ x 7 inches, pp. 146, indexed.

PHILLIPS, C. J. Glass: The Miracle Maker. (With numerous illustrations and drawings.) New York, Pitman Publishing Corp., 1941. 9¼ x 6 inches, pp. 424, indexed.

SAUZAY, A. Marvels of Glass-Making in all Ages. (Illustrated with autotypes and numerous wood engravings.) London, Sampson Low, Son, and Marston, 1870. 8 x 5⅝ inches, pp. 272.

WAUGH, Sidney. The Art of Glass Making. (Illustrated with photographs by Robert Yarnall Richie.) New York, Dodd, Mead Company, 1939. 9½ x 6¼ inches, pp. 29.